So You Think You're Smart

150 Fun and Challenging Brain Teasers

So You Think You're Smart
150 Fun and Challenging Brain Teasers

Pat Battaglia

INTERNATIONAL PUZZLE FEATURES
Specializing in clever word games for a general readership
Charlotte, NC
www.CleverPuzzles.com

So You Think You're Smart
150 Fun and Challenging Brain Teasers
by Pat Battaglia

LCCN: 2001099509

ISBN: 0-9708253-1-5

Published by
International Puzzle Features
4507 Panther Place, Charlotte, NC 28269
(704) 921-1818
www.CleverPuzzles.com

Printed in the United States of America

Thirteenth printing

Second edition

This copy of *So You Think You're Smart—150 Fun and Challenging Brain Teasers* is presented to

____

name

as a gift from

____

on this day of______________________________

date

because the aforementioned individual . . .

- ☐ is so smart.
- ☐ thinks he/she is so smart.
- ☐ thinks I think he/she is so smart.
- ☐ thinks (sometimes).
- ☐ thinks on rare occasions.
- ☐ needs all the practice thinking he/she can get.

Acknowledgments

There are many people to thank for helping make this book possible. First are the newspaper editors that have published my "If You're So Smart . . ." weekly column from which the puzzles in this book are derived. Then there are the readers of my feature. It is the interest that they have shown that has given me the incentive to constantly seek and develop new puzzles.

A thank you is extended to my mother-in-law, Constance Kirwan, for helping to title the puzzles in this book.

I would also like to thank Frank Mariani for the fine illustrations that he graciously contributed.

Most of all, I am grateful to my wife, Maralee, for her support of my avocation. Not only has she been my constant source of encouragement, she has also been the testing ground and proofreader for virtually all my puzzles.

WANTED
MIND GAMES
alias: PUZZLES
DESCRIPTION: ORIGINAL, ENTERTAINING AND CLEVER
WANTED FOR: PUBLISHING IN NEWSPAPERS AND/OR BOOK
REWARD
$5.00 FOR EACH PUZZLE SELECTED FOR PUBLICATION
AND
YOUR NAME IN PRINT AS A CONTRIBUTOR
BE ON THE LOOKOUT!
REPORT ALL INFORMATION TO:
PAT BATTAGLIA
4507 PANTHER PLACE
CHARLOTTE, NC 28269
SORRY... ACKNOWLEDGEMENTS OF CONTRIBUTIONS CANNOT BE MADE EXCEPT FOR THOSE SELECTED FOR PUBLICATION.

Contributors

The individuals listed below have contributed puzzles to me that are reprinted in this book. The puzzles were submitted in response to my newspaper column offer to pay $5 for each one selected for publication. In addition to the cash awards, each person has been sent a complimentary copy of *So You Think You're Smart—150 Fun and Challenging Brain Teasers*.

P.B.

Heather Ancora, Pittsfield, MA
Matthew Battaglia, Niagara Falls, NY
Melanie Brown, Norton, MA
Claudine Celeste, Niagara Falls, NY
Patricia Conroy, Peru, MA
Linda Dascani, Pittsfield, MA
Kathy Granieri, Niagara Falls, NY
Malcolm Hayward, Kittanning, PA
Dorothy Kidde, Nashua, NH
Edward Lindner, Adams, MA
D.S. Mandeville, Wilson, NY
Joan McGuire, McGreger, Ontario, Canada
Dorothy Nist, Kenmore, NY
Thai Pham, Pittsfield, MA
Dr. John Raymonda, Getzville, NY
Joann Reedy, Lewiston, NY
Mrs. Joann Wimbish, Bryan, TX

Introduction

So you think you're smart, huh? Okay then, hot shot, let's see you prove it. See if you can work the 150 mind games in this book.

What are *mind games*? They're unusual—sometimes even weird—challenges designed specifically to test your brain power. They're for anyone and everyone who thinks they're smart. These games are easy to understand, uncomplicated, and strictly non-technical (not a bit of mind-boggling math). There are absolutely no trick questions. The games are completely straightforward and logical. There simply is no excuse for not being able to meet their challenge. All you need is plain old "smarts." And if you do have common sense, are resourceful, and have sound reasoning, your ego will bulge.

But beware—the mind games are not the only unusual feature in this book. In fact, they're only the beginning. The way the answers are presented is unique. Each answer is given on the same page as the statement of the mind game. But to prevent it from being unavoidably read, only the mirror image is given. To further obscure the recognition of the answer, it is printed in a script lettering style instead of an easier-to-read typeface. The result is that unless you want to drive yourself cross-eyed, you will need a mirror to adjust each image for normal reading. (A mylar mirror is supplied with each paperback copy.)

Aside from being a novel approach to presenting the answers, this technique has a definite advantage: it eliminates the aggravation of paging into the back of the book in search of the appropriate answer page. It also eliminates scanning the answer page and inevitably noticing practically every answer on the page. These unsought solutions are invariably the ones that make an indelible impression on your memory. Then, when the puzzles corresponding to these remembered answers are read, the challenge and satisfaction they would have given is lost.

However, presenting the answers in the unique way they are in this book does have one drawback—you need a mirror. Simply use any mirror you have around the house, preferably a small rectangular or square one that measures no longer than the width of this page. If all else fails, use the one that every home has—the bathroom mirror. Of course, if you're not too smart you will be referring to the answers often and consequently might be spending considerable time in the bathroom. Other members of your household are sure to make some very interesting comments about that!

Using the mirror to uncover the answers is easy. Try it on the sample given below. Simply place an edge of the mirror on the line that has all the strange-looking hieroglyphics under it, with the mirror facing you. Then tilt it until you can read . . .

the answer

Yet another unusual feature is included in this book. There is a hint given with many of the mind games. When it is given, it is printed upside-down, directly below the statement of the game. Just as the mind games are of varying difficulty, so too are the hints of varying assistance. Some are very explicit. Some are fiendishly vague. Others are masked in a play on words. All of them, however, should help to some extent to get you on the right track. So if you remain baffled after trying your darndest, refer to the hint for a little help. It might be just what you need to salvage your ego and keep you out of the bathroom.

Now you have it. You know what is necessary to cope with this book. The next step is yours. Prove your smartness. Work all 150 mind games. And enjoy.

STOP
DON'T YOU DARE TRY A SINGLE PUZZLE WITHOUT FIRST READING THE INTRODUCTION! IT DESCRIBES WHAT YOU NEED TO KNOW ABOUT THIS CRAZY BOOK.

1

Working with Ease

The letter "e" was removed from ten common words. The remaining letters of each word are given below. Can you determine the ten words?

dgr	vrgrn
xcd	ndl
sntnc	lmnt
lvn	rsrv
chs	rlct

HINT: *Every word but one contains three e's.*

---

degree, exceed, sentence, eleven, cheese, evergreen, needle, element, reserve, reflect

---

2

Circular Reasoning

Each of the letter-circles given below represents a word. Each word can be spelled by starting at the appropriate letter and moving clockwise or counterclockwise around the circle. Identify the words.

Example: 

Answer: CHURCH

---

eraser, termite, alfalfa, insulin

3

Rule Out Mississippi

Name the states of the United States that consist of letters that appear only once in their spelling.

HINT: *There are nine states.*

Florida, Idaho, Iowa, Maine, New York, Texas, Utah, Vermont, Wyoming

---

4

Working Up an Appetite

A hint to each of eight common sayings that involve food is given below. Determine each saying.

Example: wage earner **Answer:** bring home the bacon

1. amateur acting	5. calm
2. embarrassed	6. cozy
3. top executive	7. influence
4. a city	8. in trouble

1. ham it up 2. egg on your face 3. the big cheese 4. the Big Apple 5. cool as a cucumber 6. warm as toast 7. butter up 8. in a pickle

5

Follow the Letter

What is the next letter of the following sequence of letters?

J A S O N ?

HINT: *The sequence involves names, but not boys names.*

The sequence represents the first letters of the months beginning with July. The missing letter is therefore D for December.

6

Put Them in Their Place

Place the nine letters B, C, G, T, Y, A, I, and two E's in the nine squares given below such that three-letter words are spelled both horizontally and vertically. Use all nine letters, one letter to a square. Three words are spelled horizontally (left to right) and three words are spelled vertically (top to bottom). All words are well-known.

B		
A	C	E
G		

HINT: *The center square contains the letter C.*

The lines as read from left to right are as follows: top line: big, middle line: ace, last line: yet.

7

A Sporting Proposition

With only eight exceptions, all the professional major league football, basketball, baseball, and hockey teams have a "second" name that ends in an "s". For example, New York Yankees. Can you name the eight exceptions?

Miami Heat, Orlando Magic, Utah Jazz, (basketball teams), Boston Red Sox, and Chicago White Sox (baseball teams), Colorado Avalanche, Minnesota Wild, Tampa Bay Lightning (hockey teams)

8

A Common Problem

What unique quality do each of the following words have in common?

calmness
defer
first
hijack
nope
roughing
stupid

HINT: *It's as simple as abc.*

Each word contains three consecutive letters in alphabetical order. For example, caLMNess.

9

Gopher It

Some words and phrases begin with the name of an animal but have a meaning that has little or nothing to do with the animal. For example, the exclamation "dog-gone." From the hint given below, identify the words or phrases all beginning with an animal name.

1. hairdo	6. domineer a husband
2. condiment	7. disease
3. metal	8. forty winks
4. untrained hair	9. coloring
5. timid	10. beat severely

1. pony tail or pig tail 2. horseradish 3. pig iron 4. cowlick 5. coward 6. henpeck 7. chicken pox 8. cat nap 9. pigment 10. lambaste

10

Widget Weighing Wisdom

There are 10 barrels with several hundred widgets in each barrel. Each widget is marked to identify what barrel it is from. All widgets look identical and weigh exactly one pound, except those in one of the barrels all weigh exactly 17 ounces each. By doing only one weighing on a scale graduated in pounds and ounces, determine which barrel contains the overweight widgets.

Place the following on the scale: one widget from the first barrel, two from the second barrel, three from the third, etc. The number of ounces greater than 55 lbs. identifies the barrel. For example, if the weight is 55 lbs. & 6 ozs., the sixth barrel contains the odd widgets.

11

Figure This

The figure below is made up of sixteen equal-length lines. Remove four of these sixteen sides and leave only four equal triangles (with no sides left over).

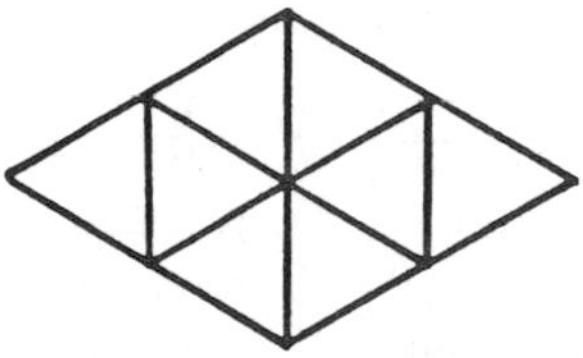

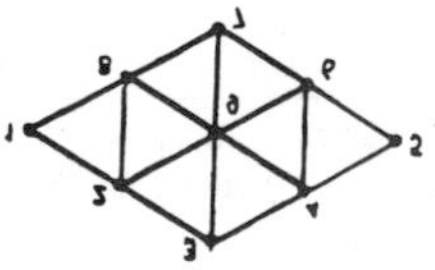

Remove sides 2-3, 2-9, 6-7, and 6-9.

12

Fractured Frazes

The wording of the following six well-known sayings has been changed to obscure their recognition. Can you identify the sayings?

1. Transport rasher to our abode.
2. Consume one's chapeau.
3. Release the feline from its cloth entrapment.
4. Yelps ascending the erroneous timber.
5. Specie in exchange for your cerebral endeavors.
6. Manufacture fodder when Sol is luminous.

---

1. Bring home the bacon. 2. Eat your hat. 3. Let the cat out of the bag. 4. Barking up the wrong tree. 5. A penny for your thoughts. 6. Make hay while the sun shines.

13

Phony Sign Language

The letters associated with the numbers on a telephone are as follows.

2	3	4	5	6	7	8	9
ABC	DEF	GHI	JKL	MNO	PRS	TUV	WXY

Place the appropriate letter corresponding to each of the numbers given below to complete the following anecdote.

Sign in a beauty parlor:

WE CURL UP AND DYE FOR YOU

9 3 2 8 7 5 8 7 2 6 3 3 9 3 3 6 7 9 6 8

we curl up and dye for you

14

A Betting Racquet

Susan and Lisa decided to play tennis against each other. They bet $1 on each game they played. Susan won three bets and Lisa won $5. How many games did they play?

HINT: *Eight is not enough.*

They played eleven games. Lisa lost three games. She had to win three additional games to break even. Then she had to win five more games to win $5. Therefore, the total number of games played is the sum of three and three and five.

15

EZ Does It

Determine what two letters, when pronounced, fit the descriptions given below.

Example: not difficult **Answer:** EZ (easy)

1. a vine
2. extra
3. a number
4. a void
5. a tent
6. a composition
7. to rot
8. surpass

---

1. IV 2. XS 3. AT 4. MT 5. TP 6. SA 7. DK 8. XL

16

Order in the Quartz

Sometimes the numbers displayed on a digital watch are in consecutive order. For example, 2:34. How many times does this occur in a twelve hour period?

HINT: *Eight is not enough.*

It occurs nine times: one twenty-three, two thirty-four, three forty-five, four fifty-six, nine ten, ten eleven, eleven twelve, twelve thirteen, and twelve thirty-four.

17

A Mental Block

Each of the four blocks shown below is marked identically. One side of each block has no marking on it. Determine the arrangement of markings on one block.

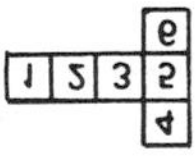

side 1: X, side 2: vertical lines, side 3: dot, side 4: horizontal lines, side 5: no marking, side 6: black

18

Ferret Out

Corresponding to each word or phrase given below is another word, similar in meaning, which is also the name of an animal. Identify these words.

Example: lifting device **Answer:** crane

1. club
2. guide
3. endure
4. bond together
5. skin blemish
6. annoy
7. bishop
8. enormous

1. bat 2. steer 3. bear 4. seal
5. mole 6. badger 7. cardinal 8. mammoth

19

Common Cents

What can be purchased at a hardware store and is priced similar to the schedule shown below? (They are common items.)

1 costs $ .50
12 costs $1.00
144 costs $1.50

HINT: *Chances are your house is equipped with a number of these items.*

The items are house numbers. Each digit costs fifty cents.

20

Sound Off

Which word doesn't belong in the following list and why?

write	heard
lead	right
waste	card
sight	waist
herd	site
led	

The word is card. It is the only word that doesn't have another word in the list pronounced like it.

21

The Fame Game

Some well-known people throughout history have been known by a single name. Galileo, for example. The first letter to six such names are given below along with a word associated with the activity that made the personality famous. Name each person.

1. M________ art
2. C________ lover
3. C________ queen
4. C________ philosopher
5. T________ music
6. S________ strength

---

1. Michelangelo 2. Casanova 3. Cleopatra
4. Confucius 5. Tschaikovsky 6. Samson

22

Pocket Money

What is the fewest number of coins required to have the exact change for all possible items that cost from one cent up to and including one dollar in one-cent increments?

A total of nine coins are needed: four pennies, one nickel, two dimes, one quarter, and one half-dollar.

23
Horsesense

Below are nine horses (represented by dots) located in a square fenced meadow. Construct two more square fences so that each horse will be in a fenced area by itself.

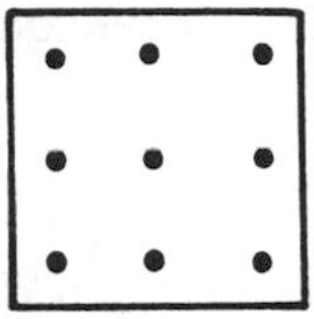

Connect the midpoint of each of the four sides with four straight lines to form one square. Then repeat the procedure on this new square to form a square around the center horse.

24
Prepared Answers

The first letters of eight well-known food combinations are given below. A hint to each combination is given in parentheses. Determine each food combination.

Example: c___ & s___ (coffee additives)
Answer: cream & sugar

1. p___ b___ & j___ (child's lunch)
2. b___ & e___ (breakfast)
3. b___ & b___ (served with meals)
4. c___ b___ & c___ (Irish dish)
5. c___ & i___ c___ (dessert)
6. c___ & c___ (snack)
7. s___ & m___ b___ (Italian dish)
8. h___ & f___ f___ (fast food)

---

1. peanut butter & jelly 2. bacon & eggs 3. bread & butter 4. corned beef & cabbage 5. cake & ice cream 6. cheese & crackers 7. spaghetti & meat-balls 8. hamburger & french fries

25

A Message Monstrosity

Insert the letters A and E into the appropriate places below and separate the words to get an interesting message.

BronFrnknstinwslonlymnbforhlrndtomkfrinds.

Baron Frankenstein was a lonely man before he learned to make friends.

26

Digit Logic

Solve the following cross-number puzzle.

HINT: *Start with "A down."*

ACROSS

A The sum of the digits is 10

C The product of the digits is 315.

D A perfect square.

F The digits read forward and backward are the same.

DOWN

A A three digit number minus 1.

B "A down" multiplied by the sum of the digits in "A down."

C Consecutively decreasing digits.

E An odd number.

A across is 910, C across is 597, D across is 81, F across is 3223, C down is 543. Solving procedure: (1) "A down" must be 99 since this is the only 2 digit number that can result by subtracting 1 from a 3 digit number (i.e., 100). (2) Determine the remaining numbers in this order: "B down", "A across", "D across", "C across", "C down", and "F across."

27

Take the Offensive

Sometimes a bland word or phrase is substituted for a blunt or offensive expression. For example, "to pass away" is often substituted for "to die." Can you identify the blunt meaning of each of the following expressions?

1. bathroom tissue
2. previously owned auto
3. inebriated
4. sanitary engineer
5. in trouble
6. intimate apparel
7. incarcerated
8. put to sleep
9. frugal
10. Montezuma's revenge

---

1. toilet paper 2. used car 3. drunk 4. garbage man 5. pregnant 6. under-wear (women's) 7. in jail 8. to kill (an animal) 9. cheap 10. diarrhea

---

28

Building with Letters

Place an appropriate letter in each square of the framework below such that every line spells a word and every column contains the same letter. One letter is given to help you.

Example:

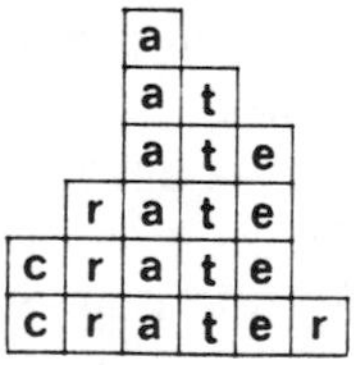

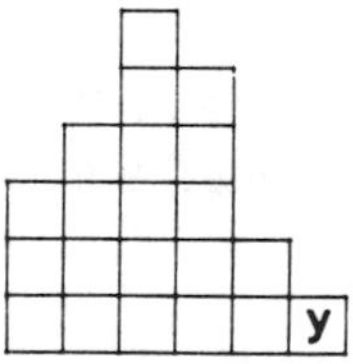

HINT: *The first letter of the bottom word is b.*

The bottom word is brandy.

29

Delinquent Detection

Five children were playing kickball. One of the five broke a window. When questioned about the incident, each child made three statements of which two were true and one was false. The statements are given below. Which child broke the window?

Joe	1. I didn't do it. 2. Sally will tell who did it. 3. One of us is in big trouble.
Matt	1. Joyce did it. 2. I didn't do it. 3. I don't even like to play kickball.
Vince	1. I didn't do it. 2. Joyce and I are good friends. 3. Sally doesn't know who did it.
Joyce	1. Matt lied when he said I broke the window. 2. I never saw Vince before today. 3. I never broke a window in my life.
Sally	1. I saw Joyce break it. 2. I didn't break the window. 3. I want to go home.

HINT: *Start with Joyce.*

Vince did it. Joyce's statements 1 and 3 must be true. If she had broken the window, both statements would have to be false. But since each child told only one lie, these two statements must be true. Therefore, Joyce's statement 2 is the one that is false. The statements of all the other children can then be proven true or false using this information.

30

Mix 'N Match

Find the one word whose meaning is similar to the first word in the pair and opposite to the second word in the pair.

Example: elevated, sober   **Answer:** high

1. remainder, right
2. maybe, weakness
3. strike, miss
4. fracture, repair
5. table, sit
6. company, soft
7. defy, mind
8. vulgar, smooth
9. midway, kind
10. land, few

---

1. left 2. might 3. hit 4. break 5. stand 6. firm 7. disobey 8. coarse 9. mean 10. lot

---

31

Robotic Reasoning

A robot is programmed to accept cool objects but reject hot objects. It accepts cookies but rejects fudge. It accepts copper but rejects aluminum. Which of the following items will the robot accept and why?

plastic	bread	letter
rubber	butter	telegram
books	rod	coffee
magazines	reel	tea

HINT: *The robot's name is Spellman.*

The robot accepts items that have double letters in the word: rubber, books, butter, reel, letter, coffee.

32

A Simple Arrangement

Arrange the blocks shown below to form a three-digit number that can be divided by seven with zero remainder.

HINT: *Try viewing the puzzle from a completely different angle.*

The number is nine hundred and thirty-one. The six block is turned upside-down to form a nine.

33

Things in General

A hint to each of eight familiar two-word phrases or names is given below. The first word in each phrase is "general." Determine the second word of each phrase or name.

Example: company official **Answer:** manager (general manager)

1. appliance manufacturer
2. TV program
3. doctor
4. autos
5. vote
6. retail outlet
7. well-known
8. inducing unconsciousness

---

1. Electric 2. Hospital 3. practitioner 4. Motors 5. election 6. store 7. knowledge 8. anesthetic

34

Watch Out

John planned to get to work ten minutes early. He thought his watch was ten minutes slow but actually it was fifteen minutes fast. Was John early, late, or on time for work?

John was thirty-five minutes early. He arrived at work when his watch read twenty minutes before the starting time. However, because his watch was fast, the correct time was fifteen minutes before the time shown on his watch.

35

Die Determining

Shown below are three identical dice in three different positions. Determine what number is on the side opposite the one. What number is opposite the four? What number is opposite the five?

The six is opposite the one, the three is opposite the four, and the two is opposite the five.

36

Body Work

A hint to each of 10 well-known phrases that include a part of the human body is given below. Determine the phrases.

Example: be aware **Answer:** Keep your eye on the ball.

1. snub
2. troublesome
3. kidding
4. bear up
5. look sharp
6. depressed
7. don't despair
8. bold
9. practical standard
10. candid

---

1. cold shoulder 2. pain in the neck 3. pulling your leg 4. keep a stiff upper lip 5. keep your eyes peeled 6. down in the mouth 7. keep your chin up 8. stick your neck out 9. rule of thumb 10. make no bones about it

---

37

Unforgettable

Form a familiar two-word phrase using the letters given in the pyramid below.

B
R R
M M M
E E E E

HINT: *Study the letter pyramid and try to remember the phrase.*

The phrase is: remember me.

38

Common Ground

What do the following eight words have in common?

diamond	lane
field	ring
court	track
table	course

HINT: *Think hard. The answer's bound to surface.*

They are names of the playing surface for eight different sports. (diamond—baseball, field—football, court—basketball, table—ping-pong, lane—bowling, ring—boxing, track—running, course—golf)

39

Cast a Spell

How do you spell the plural form of the following ten words?

1. county	6. sheep
2. hero	7. brother-in-law
3. stimulus	8. tomato
4. mouse	9. leaf
5. thief	10. fish

---

1. counties 2. heroes 3. stimuli 4. mice 5. thieves 6. sheep 7. brothers-in-law 8. tomatoes 9. leaves 10. fish

40

A Carload Sale

An automobile dealer sold 60 cars during a six-day sale. Each day the dealer sold four more cars than he did on the previous day. How many cars were sold on the first day?

None. The sum of the number of cars sold in excess of the first day's total is 4 + 8 + 12 + 16 + 20 = 60. Because this total is the exact number of cars sold, there could not have been any cars sold the first day.

41

Divide and Conquer

Divide the figure below into four identical parts.

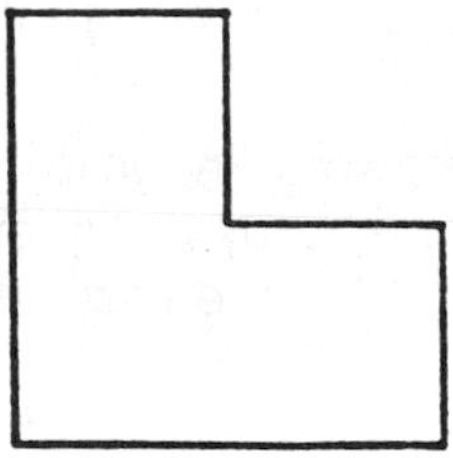

HINT: *The parts are the same shape as the figure.*

Draw a straight line between the following dots: 1-2-3-4-5-6-7, 3-8, and 5-9.

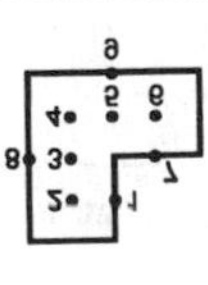

42

Animal Crackers

Represented below are eight common sayings that involve animals. The first letter of the two missing words in each saying is given. Determine the sayings.

Example: e____ as a b____ **Answer:** eager as a beaver

1. s___ as a s____
2. s___ as a f____
3. b___ as an e___
4. s___ as a m____
5. s ____as a b____
6. w____ as an o___
7. g ____ as a b____
8. m___ as a l____

1. slow as a snail 2. sly as a fox 3. big as an elephant 4. stubborn as a mule 5. strong as a bull 6. wise as an owl 7. grouchy as a bear 8. meek as a lamb

43

A Typical Word

The top row of letters of a typewriter keyboard is

Q W E R T Y U I O P

What common ten-letter word, known to anyone who understands this puzzle, can be formed by using letters selected from this group? The same letter can be used more than once.

HINT: *A hint was already given in the statement of the puzzle.*

The word is typewriter.

44

A State of Mind

Name the states of the United States that end in the letter "a".

HINT: *There are twenty-one states.*

Alabama, Alaska, Arizona, California, Florida, Georgia, Indiana, Iowa, Louisiana, Minnesota, Montana, Nebraska, Nevada, N. Carolina, N. Dakota, Oklahoma, Pennsylvania, S. Carolina, S. Dakota, Virginia, W. Virginia

---

45

Sexy Words

The masculine gender of ten words are given below. Determine the corresponding feminine gender of each word.

Example: actor **Answer:** actress

1. rooster
2. patriarch
3. stallion
4. aviator
5. stag
6. duke
7. lion
8. alumnus
9. gander
10. drake

---

1. hen 2. matriarch 3. mare 4. aviatrix 5. doe 6. duchess 7. lioness 8. alumna 9. goose 10. duck

46

Dr. No Who?

Four people were seated around a square table playing cards. The bus driver sat on Jim's left and Emma sat opposite the farmer. Dick is not the stock broker and doesn't have a driver's license. The bus driver sat opposite from Rosemarie. Who is the dentist?

Use a diagram showing the bus driver on Jim's left and Rosemarie opposite the bus driver. Because Dick doesn't have a driver's license, Emma must be the bus driver. Then, using given information, Rosemarie's the farmer, Jim's the stockbroker, and finally, Dick's the dentist.

47

Equation Transformation

Change the position of only one line to correct the following equation.

$$| - ||| = ||$$

Take one of the horizontal lines from the equal sign and place it next and parallel to the negative sign. This will change the equal sign to a negative sign and vice versa.

48

A Matter of Life or Death

A hint to each of ten words is given below. Each word begins with the sound "live" or "die." Determine each word.

Example: an organ **Answer:** liver

1. absorbent material
2. stable
3. sketch
4. a gem
5. sausage
6. talk
7. a city
8. an explosive
9. accent
10. discolored

---

1. diaper 2. livery 3. diagram 4. diamond 5. liverwurst 6. dialogue 7. Liverpool 8. dynamite 9. dialect 10. livid

---

49

Easy Reader

Read what is enclosed in each triangle. That's easy enough, isn't it?

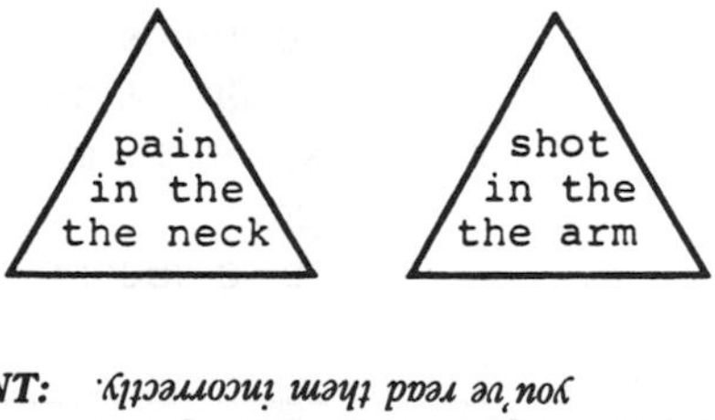

HINT: *If all you've read are familiar phrases and nothing else, you've read them incorrectly.*

The word "the" appears twice in each phrase.

50

Balance the Books

A balance scale is exactly balanced when there are three books on one side of the scale and one book and a one-half-pound weight on the other side. All books weigh the same amount. How much does one book weigh?

By removing one book from each side of the scale, two books weigh (balance with) one-half pound. Therefore, one book weighs one-quarter pound.

51

Holidaze

Name the holiday or day that is nationally observed that corresponds to each of the following.

Example: gifts **Answer:** Christmas

1. fireworks	6. costumes
2. lily	7. "I have a dream"
3. resolutions	8. summer's end
4. feasting	9. green
5. hearts	10. remembering

---

1. Independence Day 2. Easter 3. New Year's Day 4. Thanksgiving 5. Valentine's Day 6. Halloween 7. Martin Luther King, Jr.'s Birthday 8. Labor Day 9. St. Patrick's Day 10. Memorial Day

52

What's the Difference?

Which word of the following is different from the rest and why?

island	wrong
burn	salmon
foreign	hour
cocoa	lamb
knee	plumber
calf	ghost

HINT: *Review the words again. The characteristic that you are looking for is still there.*

The word burn is the only word that does not have a silent (still) letter in its spelling.

53

Darts a Possibility

How many darts must be thrown into the dart board shown below to get a score of 84?

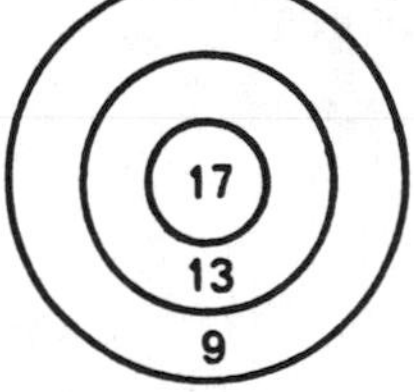

HINT: *The thrower was not an experienced dart player.*

The answer is eight darts. Only two combinations will add to eighty-four. One is five nines plus three thirteens. The other is six nines plus one seventeen plus one thirteen. Each combination consists of eight darts.

54

For Heaven's Sake

Determine the saint's name associated with each of the words given below.

Example: city **Answer:** St. Paul (Minnesota)

1. baseball	6. dog
2. parade	7. cupid
3. volcano	8. Monopoly
4. river	9. Gateway to the West
5. travel	10. Christmas

---

1. St. Louis Cardinals 2. St. Patrick 3. (Mt.) St. Helens 4. St. Lawrence 5. St. Christopher 6. St. Bernard 7. St. Valentine 8. St. Charles (place) or St. James (place) 9. St. Louis 10. St. Nicholas

---

55

Ball Games

There are several sports that are played with a ball but do not have the word "ball" in their name. Examples are billiards, pool, polo, rugby, and croquet. Can you name five more that are popular in the United States?

The sports are tennis, soccer, golf, bowling and table tennis or ping pong.

56

Time Will Tell

Sometimes the digits on a digital clock are palindromic, that is, they are the same forward as they are backward. For example, 2:12. At what times does this occur in the four-hour period from 9:00 to 1:00 o'clock.

HINT: *It occurs nine times.*

---

nine zero nine, nine nineteen, nine twenty-nine, nine thirty-nine, nine forty-nine, nine fifty-nine, ten zero one, eleven eleven, twelve twenty-one

---

57

Creature Feature

A hint to each of twelve words is given below. Each of the twelve words rhymes with a name of an animal. Determine the twelve animals.

Example: present time **Answer:** cow (rhymes with now)

1. a ground cloud
2. glove
3. an alcoholic beverage
4. hockey disk
5. above 98.6°F
6. ballot
7. a two-digit number
8. a running-track barrier
9. rough or abrasive
10. prison
11. person in monastery
12. cogitate

---

1. dog or hog 2. kitten 3. deer or steer 4. duck 5. beaver 6. goat 7. hen 8. turtle 9. horse 10. whale or quail 11. skunk 12. mink

58

Give and Take

A boy and a girl each have a bag containing the same number of jelly beans. How many jelly beans must the boy give the girl so the girl will have ten more jelly beans than the boy?

HINT: *Ten is not the answer!*

The boy must give the girl five jelly beans. He would then have five less, she would have five more, and the difference between them would be ten.

59

Shape Up

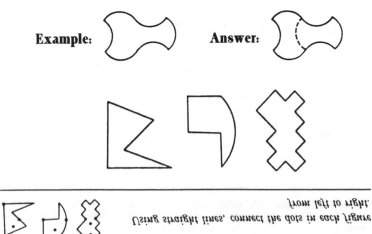

Without taking your pencil off the paper, draw a line within each figure shown below that will divide it into two identical parts.

Example: 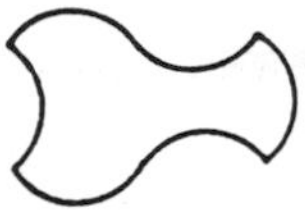 **Answer:** 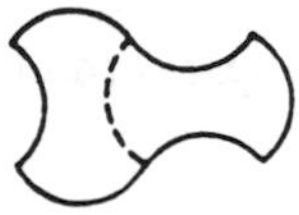

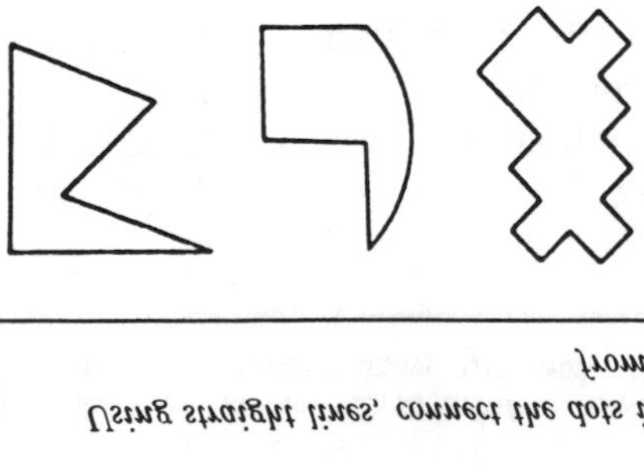

Using straight lines, connect the dots in each figure from left to right.

60

A Change for the Letter

Change one letter in each of the 10 words given below that will transform the word into an entirely different word.

Example: attach **Answer:** attack

1. slant	6. remove
2. produce	7. insert
3. until	8. quill
4. flatten	9. repair
5. gallon	10. search

---

1. slang 2. product 3. untie 4. flatter 5. gallop 6. remote 7. insect 8. quilt 9. repaid 10. starch

---

61

How Do You Do?

Four men shook hands with each other just once. How many handshakes were made?

There are six handshakes. Place the letters A, B, C, and D, representing the four men, in four corners of an imaginary square. Draw lines from each letter to the other three letters, signifying handshakes. Only six lines can be drawn.

62

The Write Stuff

Complete each sentence by adding the word that corresponds to the hint given. This word, although unrelated to the sentence, will sound like the word(s) that will make sense in the sentence.

Example: The name of_____is Robert

HINT: *Crime of starting fires.*

Answer: arson (sounds like "our son")

1. She went to the bank and asked for____.

HINT: *by yourself*

2. The colicky baby_____all night.

HINT: *without hair*

3. Everyone agreed with me____.

HINT: *dairy product*

4. Society should build more nursing homes_____people.

HINT: *used for holding papers*

5. _____when your father asked if you played hookey?

HINT: *a month*

---

1. alone (a loan) 2. bald (bawled) 3. butter (but her) 4. folder (for old-er) 5. July (d, you lie)

63

Matching Pairs

Below are the first letters of well-known people, both real and fictional, that are associated with each other. Also given is a hint to determine the names of these people. Identify the names.

Example: A____ and E____ Biblical parents
Answer: Adam and Eve

1.	H ____	and	G ____	fairy tale
2.	L ____	and	C ____	U.S. explorers
3.	P ____	and	G ____	detergent manufacturer
4.	T ____	and	J ____	cartoon characters
5.	S ____	and	D ____	Biblical twosome
6.	R ____	and	J ____	young lovers
7.	J ____	and	J ____	nursery rhyme
8.	A ____	and	C ____	comedians

---

1. Hansel & Gretel 2. Lewis & Clark 3. Proctor & Gamble 4. Tom & Jerry
5. Samson & Delilah 6. Romeo & Juliet 7. Jack & Jill 8. Abbott & Costello

---

64

A Monetary Muddle

What fifty coins have a total value of exactly one dollar?

Forty pennies, two dimes, and eight nickels

65

Tracking Triangles

How many triangles are there in the figure below?

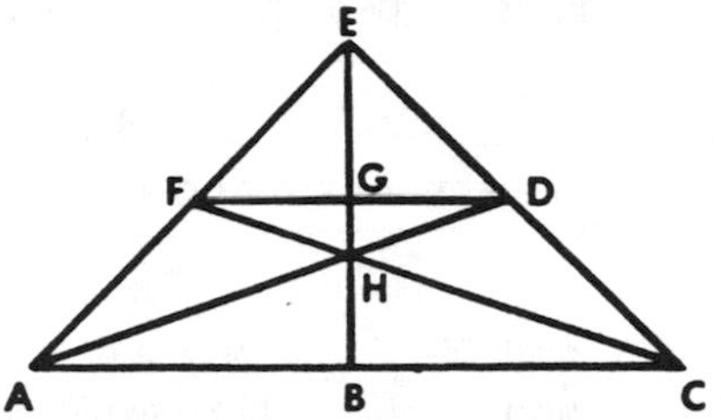

HINT: *There are more than twenty.*

There are twenty-four triangles: ABE, ABH, ACD, ACE, ACF, ACH, ADE, ADF, AEH, AFH, BCE, BCH, CDF, CDH, CEF, CEH, DEF, DEG, DEH, DFH, DGH, EFG, EFH, FGH.

66

Look at This

Given below are the meanings of 10 phrases. Each of the phrases begins with the word "look." What are the phrases?

Example: seek **Answer:** look for

1. respect
2. visit briefly
3. to take care of
4. anticipate
5. be careful
6. get active
7. examine
8. plan for the future
9. present a good appearance
10. regard with contempt

---

1. look up to 2. look in on 3. look after 4. look forward to 5. look out 6. look alive 7. look over 8. look ahead 9. look sharp 10. look down on

67

Just for Phun

If the inventor of an amplification device is considered to be Mike R. Fone, who are the inventors of the following:

1. pumpkin carving
2. a bread covered with tomato sauce, cheese and spices
3. an auditorium for athletic events
4. burglar tools
5. tables, chairs, etc. for outdoor use
6. hospital gowns

---

1. Jack O. Lantern 2. Pete Zah 3. Jim Nazium 4. Jimmy Locks 5. Patty O'Furniture 6. Seymour Butts

---

68

Common Knowledge

What characteristic is common to each of the following words?

reward	lived
rats	mug
devil	snoops
gum	star
spoons	drawer

HINT: *The characteristic is demonstrated in the opposite column*

When each word is spelled backward, it forms another word that is given in the opposite column.

69

Come Bind Words

Determine the word that can be combined with each word in the pairs below to form two new words.

Example: out, up **Answer:** let (outlet, letup)

1. worm, note
2. moon, house
3. some, shake
4. room, soft
5. law, with
6. water, rope
7. field, pop
8. try, dust

---

1. book 2. light 3. hand 4. ball 5. out 6. tight 7. corn 8. pan

---

70

State the Name

It is well-known that Texas is the Lone Star State. What states are associated with the following names?

1. Golden State
2. Ocean State
3. Sunshine State
4. Aloha State
5. First State
6. Show Me State
7. Silver State
8. Last Frontier
9. Bluegrass State
10. Grand Canyon State
11. Bay State
12. Land of Enchantment

---

1. California 2.Rhode Island 3. Florida & South Dakota 4. Hawaii 5. Delaware 6. Missouri 7. Nevada 8. Alaska 9. Kentucky 10. Arizona 11. Massachusetts 12. New Mexico

71

Dots It

Place five dots in the proper squares in the framework below such that no two dots are in line horizontally, vertically, or diagonally.

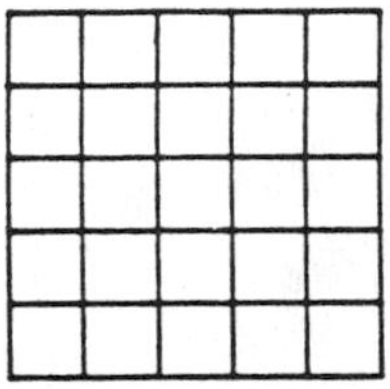

Place a dot in each of the following locations: a-1, b-4, c-2, d-5, and e-3.

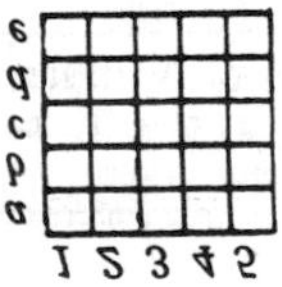

72

Junior Trivia

A young dog is called a pup. What are the young of the following animals called?

1. cat
2. bear
3. chicken
4. deer
5. goat
6. sheep
7. whale
8. goose
9. donkey
10. kangaroo

1. kitten 2. cub 3. chick 4. fawn 5. kid 6. lamb 7. calf 8. gosling 9. foal 10. joey

73

Placement Predicament

Place 10 marbles along the inside walls of a square box such that an equal number of marbles are along each of the four sides.

Place one marble in a corner and a second marble in the opposite corner. Of the remaining eight marbles, place two along each wall of the four sides.

74

Mechanical Miler

A train 1 mile long travels at the rate of 1 mile a minute through a tunnel 1 mile long. How much time will it take for the train to pass completely through the tunnel?

It takes two minutes, one minute to get completely in the tunnel and one minute to get completely out of it.

75

Easy as Pie

Represented below are common sayings with the two key words missing from each saying. The first letters of the missing words are given. A hint to the second word of each phrase is given in parentheses. Determine the phrases.

Example: g____as g____(metal) **Answer:** good as gold

1. c___ as i___ (water)
2. s___ as s___ (fabric)
3. w___ as s___ (precipitation)
4. h___ as n___ (fastener)
5. h___ as h___ (Hades)
6. g___ as s___ (offense)

---

1. cold as ice 2. smooth as silk 3. white as snow 4. hard as nails 5. hot as hell 6. guilty as sin

---

76

Those Are the Breaks

An employee begins working promptly at 8:00 a.m., has lunch from 12 noon to 1:00 p.m., and stops working at precisely 5:00 p.m. If the employee takes a 5-minute break after every half hour worked, exactly how much time is spent actually working in a single day? Assume the employee is working at all times except for breaks and lunch time.

HINT: *The employee does not take fourteen breaks.*

The time spent working is seven hours. There are a total of twelve breaks: eight thirty to eight thirty-five, nine o-five to nine ten, nine forty to nine forty-five, etc.

77

What Next?

What is the next letter of the following sequence?

B C D G J O ?

HINT: *You can get this if you shape up.*

The letter P. The sequence represents letters of the alphabet formed with curved lines.

78

Present Time

The sizes of three Christmas gift packages are small, medium, and large. Each package is wrapped with a different color paper, either red, green, or silver. There is also a different color bow on each package, either red, green, or gold. From the following two statements, determine the color of wrapping paper and bow associated with the three packages.

1. The small package has a green bow.
2. The large package is the only one without contrasting colors of bow and paper.

The only matching colors available for the large package are red paper and a red bow. The only contrasting paper color remaining for the small package is silver. The medium size package is left with green paper and a gold bow.

79

Word Without End

What single letter when added to each of the following will form three-letter words?

la__ se__ si__
ta__ he__ fo__
wa__ fi__ bo__
ve__ mi__ so__

The letter x.

80

A Borderline Case

Draw three straight lines such that a partition is formed for each of the seven dots shown below.

Draw one line under dots 1 and 3 but above dot 4. Draw the second line from between dots 1 and 2 to between dots 4 and 6. Draw the third line to the left of dots 3, 7, and 6 and to the right of dot 4.

81

Double Trouble

Find 15 common words, each of which contain one of the 15 double letters given below. For example, a word containing "bb" is ribbon.

aa bb cc dd ff gg hh ii
kk mm nn rr uu ww zz

Among the answers are: bazaar, bubble, accept, add, off, egg, hitchhiker, skiing, bookkeeper, hammer, inn, error, vacuum, powwow, puzzle.

82

Associated Problems

Determine the missing word that is associated with the following word in the same way that the words of the first pair are related.

Example: mountain: valley ___?___ :cold
Answer: hot (meanings are opposite)

1. forest: tree ___?___ :sheep
2. bald: hair ___?___ :air
3. aged: wine ___?___ :wood
4. coast: driving ___?___ :flying
5. reptile: snake ___?___ :mosquito
6. perimeter: triangle ___?___ :circle
7. lukewarm: hot ___?___ :wet

---

1. flock 2. vacuum 3. seasoned 4. glide 5. insect 6. circumference 7. moist

83

A Regular Cutup

How can you divide seven apples among 12 people such that everyone will have exactly equal portions? Each apple is not to be cut into more than four pieces.

HINT: *The apples can be cut into less than four pieces.*

Cut four apples into three pieces each. Cut the three remaining apples into four pieces each. Distribute a $\frac{1}{3}$ and a $\frac{1}{4}$ portion to each person. ($\frac{1}{3} + \frac{1}{4} = \frac{7}{12}$)

84

Seeing is Deceiving

There is something unusual about each of the 12 words listed below. What is it?

artic	labratory
existance	fourty
mathmatics	wierd
religous	incredable
temperment	maintanence

All words are misspelled. Correct spelling is: arctic, existence, mathematics, supersede, religious, temperament, laboratory, forty, weird, judgment, incredible, maintenance.

85

Colorful Sayings

A hint to each of 12 well-known words or phrases is given below. Each word or phrase contains the name of a color. Determine each word or phrase.

Example: a bird **Answer:** blue jay

1. healthy
2. despondent
3. profitable
4. very mad
5. U.S. currency
6. a crime
7. Wisconsin city
8. first prize
9. a national park
10. a salad dressing
11. witchcraft
12. bureaucracy

---

1. in the pink 2. feeling blue 3. in the black 4. seeing red 5. greenbacks 6. blackmail 7. Green Bay 8. blue ribbon 9. Yellowstone 10. blue cheese 11. black magic 12. red tape

---

86

Let's Face It

Draw two straight lines on the face of the clock shown below such that the sum of the numbers in each section are equal.

***HINT:** The lines do not intersect.*

Draw one line from between the ten and eleven to between the two and three. The second line is drawn from between the eight and nine to between the four and five.

87

A French Inquisition

All words in this unique crossword puzzle form familiar phrases when preceded by the word "French." Can you find them?

HINT: *The three longest blanks in the framework are in connection with a salad and the military.*

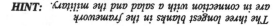

The horizontal words from top to bottom are: door, horn, pastry, Foreign Legion, kiss, Quarter, poodle. The vertical words from left to right are: cuff, Riviera, Alps, Connection, dressing, toast, fry.

88

Spellbound

Pick out the two words from the ten given below that are made up of the same letters.

brother	thereon
thereof	tremors
thermos	theorem
bothers	mothers
clothes	brothel

The two words are thermos and mothers.

89

Unlikely Similarities

Determine the word that is similar in meaning to each word in the pair given below.

Example: brain, behave **Answer:** mind

1. tied, leap
2. rapid, abstain
3. company, solid
4. nasty, average
5. container, jolt
6. type, gentle
7. similar, enjoy
8. level, apartment
9. strength, maybe
10. student, eye
11. tilt, end
12. conceal, skin

---

1. bound 2. fast 3. firm 4. mean 5. jar 6. kind 7. like 8. flat 9. might 10. pupil 11. tip 12. hide

---

90

Triple Time

At what times does a digital watch display at least three identical digits in consecutive order in a 12-hour period? For example, one of the times is 2:22. (The watch indicates hours and minutes but not seconds.)

HINT: *There are seventeen times.*

---

one eleven, two twenty-two, three thirty-three, four forty-four, five fifty-five, ten o'clock, eleven ten through eleven nineteen, and twelve twenty-two

91

Murky Math

What common symbol used in arithmetic when placed between the numbers four and five will result in a number that is greater than four but less than six?

HINT: *This straightforward question deserves a pointed answer.*

The symbol is a decimal point.

92

Agelong Words

What word ending in "age" is associated with each of the ten words given below.

Example: suitcases **Answer:** baggage

1. platform
2. harm
3. tube-shaped food
4. to bleed
5. salary
6. speech
7. any drink
8. path
9. fierce
10. animal enclosure

---

1. stage 2. damage 3. sausage 4. hemorrhage 5. wage 6. language
7. beverage 8. passage 9. savage 10. cage

93

Cut a Mean Carpet

Shown below is a non-reversible rug with a cross-shaped hole in the center. Cut the rug into two pieces such that they can be arranged to form a rectangular rug without a hole.

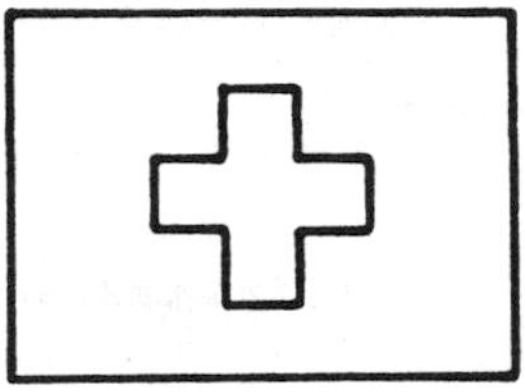

HINT: *The shape of the two cuts are identical and each cut consists of two straight lines.*

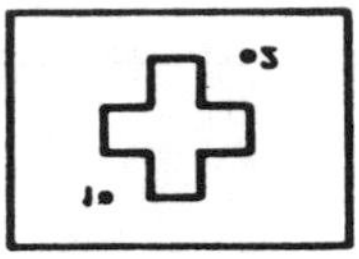

The shape of the cut is formed as follows: Draw a horizontal line from point 1 to the top edge of the cross. Draw a vertical line from point 1 to the top edge of the rug. Similarly, draw two lines from point 2: a horizontal line to the bottom edge of the cross and a vertical line to the bottom edge of the rug.

94

Sentence Me

The same letter is missing seventeen times in the apparent jumble of letters given below. Determine this letter, insert it in the appropriate places, and separate the words formed to make a sensible sentence.

HGRTDTHLVNXTRMLYWLLDRSSDGNTLMN

HINT: *You should find the missing letter with ease.*

He greeted the eleven, extremely well-dressed gentlemen.

95

Dealing with Pros

A hint to each of 10 words is given below. When each of these 10 words is preceded by "pro," a new word is formed. Determine the 10 words beginning with "pro."

Example: a large measure of weight
Answer: proton (*ton* is the large measure of weight)

1. opposite of lost
2. a farm vehicle
3. water surrounding a castle
4. a tube or pipe
5. a part
6. a male's first name beginning with V.
7. examination
8. a small measure of weight
9. an abrasive tool
10. U.S. province

---

1. profound 2. protractor 3. promote 4. product 5. proportion 6. province
7. protest 8. program 9. profile 10. prostate

96

A Dandy Garden

A dandelion is growing in a garden. In 30 days the garden will be completely covered with the weed. Assuming that dandelions double in number every day, how many days are required to completely cover the garden when there are two dandelions on the first day instead of one?

The answer is twenty-nine days. Starting with two dandelions is the same condition as the second day when beginning with one dandelion.

97

Wild Cards

Three playing cards are placed face down on a card table as shown below. Identify each card based on the following information.

1. A heart is to the left of a club.
2. A diamond is to the left of a six.
3. One card is an ace.
4. A jack is to the left of a heart.

By analyzing facts 1 and 4, the order, from left to right, is jack, heart, and club. From fact 2, the jack is a diamond and the heart is a 6. From fact 3, the club is an ace.

98

Name the Character

Some famous and infamous people throughout history have been known by a single name followed by the word "the" and then a word that represents a distinguishing characteristic about the person. Given below are the first letters of both the name and the distinguishing characteristic of five people. Can you identify them?

Example: H____the E____ **Answer:** Henry the Eighth

1. J____the R____
2. A____the G____
3. A____the H____
4. J____the B____
5. B____the K____

HINT: *All are men.*

---

1. Jack the Ripper 2. Alexander the Great 3. Attila the Hun 4. John the Baptist 5. Billy the Kid

99

Stargazing

Find seven, 5-point stars in the figure below.

100

Food for Thought

Fill in the blanks in the story below with eight different words (some are slang) that not only have a meaning that fits into context but also are edible substances.

My wife and I were looking at cars at a used car lot. I pointed to a sedan and said to her, "__1__, would you like to test drive this car? It looks like a__2__to me." She suggested pricing the car first, so I talked to a salesman. We had a__3__over how much__4__he wanted for the car. The discussion turned into a__5__. I said to my wife, "Let's go. This guy's a__6__! The car is probably a__7__anyway." My wife thought the man was full of__8__, too.

1. honey 2. peach 3. beef 4. bread or dough 5. rhubarb 6. nut or pill 7. lemon 8. baloney

101

Rhyme & Reason

Find the word that rhymes with the first word in the pair and is opposite in meaning to the second word in the pair.

Example: thunder, over **Answer:** under

1. find, disobey
2. one, all
3. cop, success
4. said, tail
5. more, ceiling
6. party, frail
7. test, exercise
8. dial, frown
9. mess, strip
10. boil, play

---

1. mind 2. none 3. flop 4. head 5. floor 6. hearty 7. rest 8. smile 9. dress 10. toil

---

102

Common Unusual Words

All the words below share an unusual trait. What is it?

first	dirty
belt	begin
glow	film
almost	ghost
city	abhor

HINT: *The trait is evident when you get your thoughts in order.*

The letters of the spelling of each word are in alphabetical order.

103

A Stately Problem

Name all states of the United States that are spelled using only four letters of the alphabet. The names may be more than four letters long but contain only four different letters.

HINT: *There are nine states.*

The states are Iowa, Utah, Alaska, Alabama, Kansas, Mississippi, Tennessee, Indiana, and Hawaii.

104

It's All Relative

Determine a fifth word that is related to each group of four words.

Example: **sleeping, contest, mark, shop**
Answer: **beauty (sleeping beauty, beauty contest, beauty mark, beauty shop)**

1. name, pig, knife, ink
2. lie, snow, elephant, wash
3. worm, story, end, store
4. rest, bug, hospital, room
5. boy, soft, mark, tight
6. ribbon, royal, cross, bonnet

---

1. pen 2. white 3. book 4. bed 5. water 6. blue

105

Wreck Tangles

How many rectangles are there in the figure below?

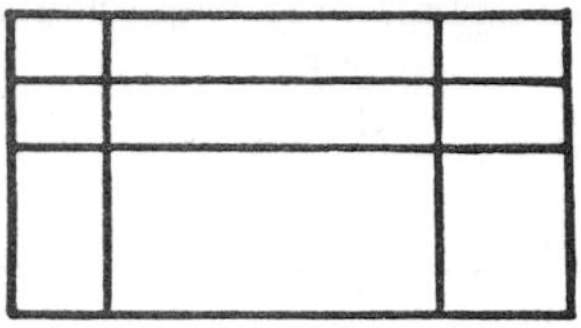

There are thirty-six: nine single rectangles, twelve consisting of two smaller rectangles, six consisting of three each, four consisting of four each, four of six each, and one of nine.

106

A Reasonable Arrangement

The numbers 1 through 12 are placed into four groups given below. Why were the numbers in each group chosen for that particular group?

Group #1	Group #2	Group #3	Group #4
1	4	3	11
2	5	7	12
6	9	8	
10			

HINT: *You'll be spellbound by the answer.*

Each group has the same number of letters in the spelling of its numbers. Three letter words in the first group, four letter words in the second group, etc.

107

A Hot Job

A hint to the second half to each of 10 words or phrases beginning with "hot" is given below. Determine the words and phrases.

Example: vegetable **Answer:** hot potato

1. animal
2. chair
3. dwelling
4. dessert
5. dish
6. skull
7. weapon discharge
8. shaft
9. thin mark
10. material

---

1. hot dog 2. hot seat 3. hothouse 4. hot cake 5. hot plate 6. hothead 7. hot shot 8. hot rod 9. hotline 10. hot stuff

---

108

The Law of Averages

A man drove 120 miles at an average speed of 60 mph. On the return trip he traveled exactly the same route and averaged 40 mph. What was his average speed for the round trip?

HINT: *Fifty mph is not the answer.*

The average speed was forty-eight mph. The average speed is determined by dividing the total distance traveled (240 miles) by the total travel time (5 hours: 2 going plus 3 returning).

109

A Race with Time

Two stopwatches were used to measure the time of a race. The watches were started simultaneously at the beginning of the race and stopped simultaneously at the end of the race. One watch ran 2 seconds per minute fast and the other ran 1 second per minute slow. At the end of the race the difference in the measured times was exactly 1 minute. What was the exact length of time of the race?

The race lasts exactly twenty minutes. One watch was 3 sec/min faster than the other. The time required to get a one minute (60 sec) difference is 60 sec divided by 3 sec/min which is twenty minutes.

110

Trite as Can Be

Represented below are common sayings with two key words missing from each saying. The first letters of the missing words are given. A hint to the second word of each saying is given in parentheses. Determine the sayings.

Example: n____as a f____(dessert)

Answer: nutty as a fruitcake

1. s____ as a d____ (animal)
2. s____ as a t____ (nail)
3. f____ as a p____ (flapjack)
4. c____ as a w____ (shrill)
5. s____ as an a____ (projectile)
6. p____ as a p____ (image)
7. b____ as a b____ (insect)
8. s____ as a w____ (flog)

---

1. sick as a dog 2. sharp as a tack 3. flat as a pancake 4. clean as a whistle 5. straight as an arrow 6. pretty as a picture 7. busy as a bee 8. smart as a whip

111

Made to Order

In what order are the following sports listed?

soccer
hockey
football
baseball
bowling
golf

HINT: *Golf is last because it has the most.*

The order is of increasing number of playing periods or sections: two halves in soccer, three periods in hockey, four quarters in football, nine innings in baseball, ten frames in bowling, and eighteen holes in golf.

112

Square Route

Draw the three squares shown below with one continuous line without lifting your pencil from the paper and without crossing or redrawing any line.

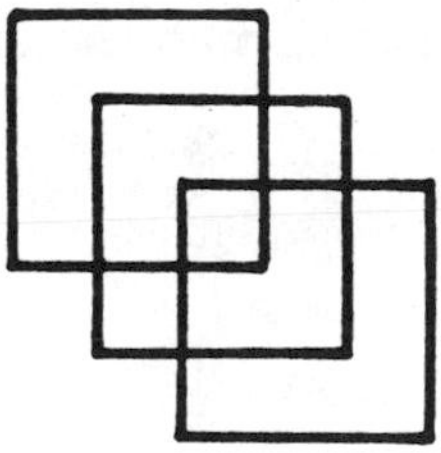

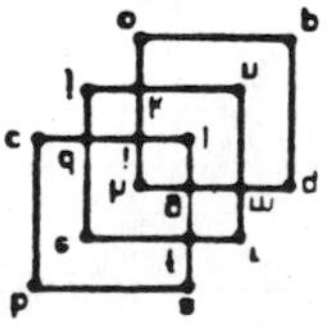

The path is as follows: a-b-c-d-e-f-g-h-i-d-j-k-i-l-g-m-n-k-o-p-q-m-r-f-a.

113

In a Spell

Corresponding to each of the 10 hints given below is a word with "ang" in its spelling. Identify the 10 words.

Example: a fruit **Answer:** orange

1. pointed tooth
2. heavenly spirit
3. informal words
4. peril
5. stable
6. mad
7. put in order
8. alter
9. speech
10. intertwine

---

1. fang 2. angel 3. slang 4. danger 5. manger 6. angry 7. arrange 8. change 9. language 10. tangle

---

114

Family Ties

How many sons and daughters does a man have if each of the man's sons has twice as many sisters as brothers and each of the daughters has just as many sisters as brothers?

The man has three sons and four daughters.

115

Sum Triangle

Place the numbers 4 through 9 along the sides of the triangle below such that the numbers along each side (including the given numbers 1, 2, and 3) add to 17.

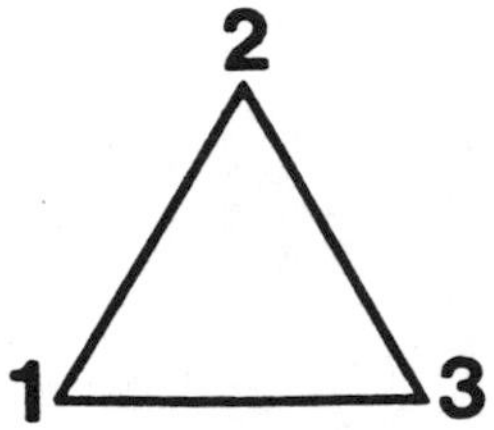

The digits five and nine are on the side between the one and two, four and eight are between the two and three, and the six and seven are between the one and three.

116

The Opposite Attraction

Determine the word that is opposite in meaning to each of the words given below:

Example: raise **Answer:** lower

1. lift	6. harvest
2. yea	7. punctual
3. dilate	8. inflate
4. explode	9. dilute
5. lend	10. resistant

---

1. drop 2. nay 3. contract 4. implode 5. borrow 6. sow or plant 7. tardy 8. deflate 9. concentrate 10. susceptible

117

An Abbrev. Puzzle

Can you identify common two-letter abbreviations, excluding those of proper names, that begin with the letters A through M? For example, an abbreviation beginning with A is AC (alternating current).

Among the answers are: AM (radio band), B.C. (before Christ), CB (citizen's band), DC (direct current), ea. (each), ft. (feet), GI (soldier), hr. (hour), in. (inch), jr. (junior), km (kilometer), LP (long playing), M.D. (doctor).

118

A One Liner

Change the location of only one line in the arrangement below to make the sum equal to 4.

$$| + || + ||| + |||| = 4$$

HINT: *An astrologer would refer you to your sign.*

Remove the vertical line from the left most positive sign and place it horizontally in front of the one. This will result in a negative sign in front of the first two numerals.

119

Triple Play

A hint to each of eight well-known groups of three words is given below. Determine the three-word groups.

Example: national colors **Answer:** red, white & blue

1. Disney characters
2. dimensions
3. God
4. time
5. sandwich
6. matter
7. basic education
8. Christmas gifts

---

1. Huey, Dewey & Louie 2. length, width & height 3. Father, Son & Holy Spirit 4. past, present & future 5. bacon, lettuce & tomato 6. solid, liquid & gas 7. reading, writing & arithmetic 8. gold, frankincense & myrrh

---

120

Odd Word Out

Which word of the 10 given below is different from the other nine and why?

mom	refer
peep	pop
better	redder
rotor	boob
nun	madam

HINT: *The difference is not grammatical.*

The word better is different from the rest. It is the only word that is not spelled the same backward as it is forward.

121

Delicious Dilemma

An ice cream parlor served 100 hot fudge sundaes. Twelve of the customers had ice cream and hot fudge only. Fifty-eight customers had whipped cream on their sundaes and seventy-three customers had chopped nuts on theirs. How many customers had sundaes with whipped cream and chopped nuts?

Forty-three. Of the 88 customers that had whipped cream and/or chopped nuts, 30 had no whipped cream (88 − 58 = 30) and 15 had no chopped nuts (88 − 73 = 15). Therefore, 43 customers did have both whipped cream and chopped nuts (88 − 30 − 15 = 43).

122

Symbol To Solve

What is the next symbol in the following sequence?

Look at one-half of the puzzle— the right half of course! **HINT:**

The sequence is the letters A through F. The right hand portion of each symbol is the letter and the left hand portion is its mirror image. Therefore, Ŧ is the next symbol.

123

Go To It

Can you name nine words beginning in a "to" sound that have an increasing number of letters from 2 through 10?

---

to, too or two, tool or tomb, today or tooth, toupee or touché, tonight or twosome, tomorrow or together, toothache or toothpick, toothpaste or toothbrush

---

124

Palindromic Pondering

Associated with each hint below is a word that is spelled the same backward as it is forward. Such a word is called a palindrome. Find all 10 palindromes.

Example: male parent **Answer:** dad

1. young dog
2. boy's nick name
3. religious career
4. past tense of do
5. firecracker that failed to explode
6. a body part
7. expression of amazement
8. young child
9. a joke
10. baby's wear

HINT: *All are three-letter words.*

---

1. pup 2. Bob 3. nun 4. did 5. dud 6. eye 7. wow 8. tot 9. gag 10. bib

125

Counting Confusion

How many cubes are there in the figure below?

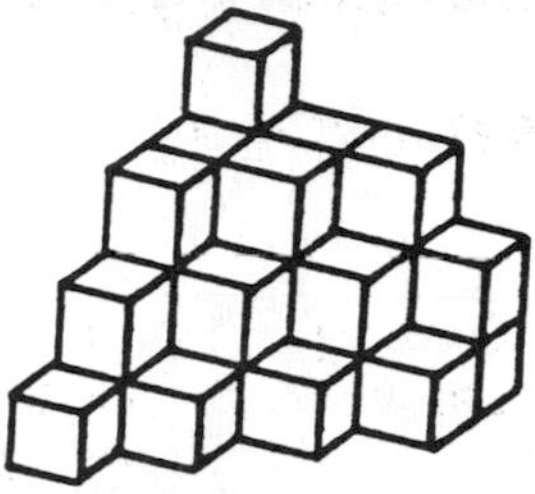

There are thirty-one cubes.

126

Threesomes

At what times during a 12 hour day do the digits of a digital clock add to 3? The clock indicates hours and minutes only (not seconds). For example, 10:02 is one of the times.

HINT: *There are twelve times.*

ten zero two, ten eleven, ten twenty, eleven zero one, eleven ten, twelve o'clock, one zero two, one eleven, one twenty, two zero one, two ten, and three o'clock.

127

The Name Game

Determine a person's first name or nickname that corresponds to each of the meanings given below.

Example: legal proceeding **Answer:** Sue

1. paper currency
2. straight forward
3. steal
4. harass
5. lifting device
6. burglar's tool
7. legal document
8. beauty of motion

---

1. Bill 2. Frank 3. Rob 4. Harry 5. Jack 6. Jimmy 7. Will 8. Grace

---

128

A Separate Problem

The same letter is missing fifteen times in the apparent jumble of letters given below. Determine this letter, insert it in the appropriate places, and separate the words formed to uncover a factual statement.

nrdvrk'smmmlththsshrpclwsndttcksnts

HINT: *A word to the wise is sufficient.*

An aardvark's a mammal that has sharp claws and attacks ants.

129

Sum Path

Start in the square indicated and find the path to the end square such that the sum of the numbers in the path is 100. The numbers in the start and end squares are to be included in the sum of 100. The path from one square to another must be horizontal or vertical (not diagonal).

			end
13	10	41	9
0	2	15	16
5	11	6	8
20	4	17	13
start			

twenty—five—zero—thirteen—ten—two—eleven—six—eight—sixteen—nine

130

A Colorful Challenge

Given below are colors that represent the first word of two-word phrases. A hint to each phrase is also given. Identify each phrase.

Example: blue____(clothing) **Answer:** jeans

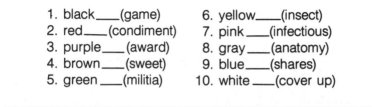

1. black____(game)
2. red____(condiment)
3. purple____(award)
4. brown____(sweet)
5. green____(militia)
6. yellow____(insect)
7. pink____(infectious)
8. gray____(anatomy)
9. blue____(shares)
10. white____(cover up)

1. jack 2. pepper 3. heart 4. sugar 5. beret 6. jacket 7. eye 8. matter 9. chip 10. wash

131

Choosing Sides

Reposition three sides from the figure below and get five triangles.

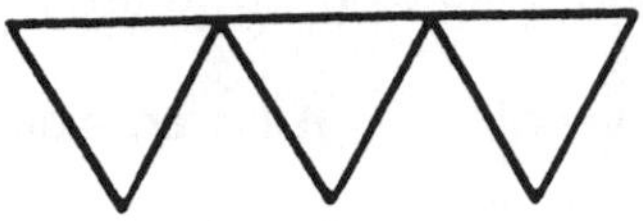

HINT: *All triangles are not the same size.*

Remove the triangle from the right end or the left end. Place it such that its horizontal base connects the lowest two points of the two remaining triangles.

132

A Borderline Mind

Name all the states that border on the Atlantic Ocean.

HINT: *There are fourteen states.*

Maine, New Hampshire, Massachusetts, Rhode Island, Connecticut, New York, New Jersey, Delaware, Maryland, Virginia, North Carolina, South Carolina, Georgia, Florida

133

Doggone

There is a well-known saying similar in meaning to each of the phrases given below. Each saying has the word "dog" or "dogs" in it. What are the eight sayings?

Example: very ill **Answer:** sick as a dog

1. a rain storm
2. too old to learn
3. sultry summer period
4. ignored for misbehavior
5. allow to deteriorate
6. everyone will eventually get a time of power or glory
7. every man for himself
8. to be sophisticated or assume airs

---

1. raining cats and dogs 2. can't teach an old dog new tricks 3. dog days 4. in the dog house 5. going to the dogs 6. every dog has his day 7. dog eat dog 8. put on the dog

---

134

Gimme Five

Form five common words using the letters, a, e, p, r, and s. Each word must be five letters long and contain all the given letters.

HINT: *Three of the words are plurals.*

The words are pears, reaps, rapes, spare, and spear.

135

A Creature Quandary

The following animals are listed in alphabetical order according to a certain characteristic. What is this characteristic?

sheep
dog
hen
rooster
cat
cow
pig
duck

HINT: *This sounds like a more difficult puzzle than it is.*

The characteristic is the sound attributed to each animal. (baa—sheep, bowwow—dog, cluck—hen, etc.)

136

U Name It

Determine the phrase that is associated with each given condition. One word of the phrase is similar in meaning to the given word. The other word, corresponding to the space, sounds like a letter of the alphabet.

Example: ______ blouse **Answer:** tee shirt

1. frozen ___
2. aqua ___
3. ___ beam
4. dark ___
5. crimson ___
6. ___ myself
7. stitching ___
8. divide ___
9. ___ molars
10. sweet ___

---

1. iced tea 2. blue jay 3. x-ray 4. black eye 5. Red Sea 6. why me ; or see me 7. sewing bee 8. split pea 9. eye teeth 10. honey bee

137

Clowning Around

Harry, Larry, and Terry work in a circus as ringmaster, lion tamer, and clown—not necessarily in that order. Given the following facts, determine who is the clown.

1. Terry's red circus clothes match his hair coloring.
2. Tomorrow Larry is scheduled to get a permanent by his hairdresser, Kerry.
3. The ringmaster is two inches taller than Larry.
4. The lion tamer's nickname is Baldie.

Solution: The real name of Baldie, the lion tamer, must be Harry because Terry and Larry both have hair. The ringmaster must be Terry, because by statement 3, he's not Larry. Larry is therefore the clown.

138

Peer Amid

Determine the number of cannon balls (all the same size) that are stacked in the three-sided pyramid shown below.

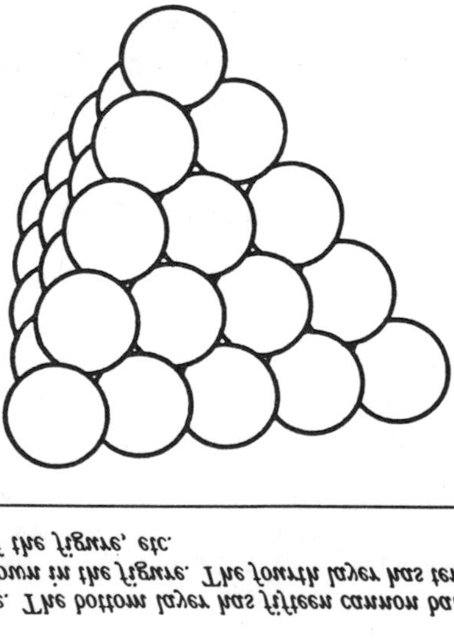

There are thirty-five. The bottom layer has fifteen cannon balls arranged like the one complete side shown in the figure. The fourth layer has ten balls arranged like the top four rows of the figure, etc.

139

Rhyme Time

Determine a two-word rhyme similar in meaning to each of the phrases given below.

Example: nasty boy **Answer:** bad lad

1. angry supervisor
2. obese kitten
3. warm pan
4. seafood plate
5. blond wig
6. spendid combo
7. bossy girl
8. monkey shawl
9. recipe collection
10. artificial stone
11. domestic rodent
12. intoxicated cleric

---

1. cross boss 2. fat cat 3. hot pot 4. fish dish 5. fair hair 6. grand band 7. sassy lassie 8. ape cape 9. cook book 10. mock rock 11. house mouse 12. drunk monk

---

140

Tea Time

Can you name 15 common six letter words that have a "tt" in the middle of them? For example, "better."

Among the words are butter, letter, mitten, matter, button, cotton, sitter, kitten, rotten, batter, gutter, litter, bitter, putter, little, mutter, cutter, mutton, bitten, and wetter.

141

A Tiring Trip

A car traveled 50,000 miles. Five tires were used equally in accumulating these miles. How many miles usage did each tire get?

Each tire was used for forty thousand miles. The calculations are as follows: 50,000 miles × 4 tires = 200,000 tire miles, 200,000 tire miles ÷ 5 tires = 40,000 miles per tire.

142

For Letter Words

A hint to each of 12 common words beginning with the letters "for" is given below. Determine the 12 words.

Example: always **Answer:** forever

1. prohibit
2. a car
3. pardon
4. alien
5. previous
6. classy dance
7. utinsel
8. building
9. riches
10. imitation
11. shape
12. recipe

---

1. forbid 2. Ford 3. forgive 4. foreigner 5. former 6. formal 7. fork 8. fort 9. fortune 10. forgery 11. form 12. formula

143

Time Out

A clock runs 5 minutes slow every hour. The clock was set at the proper time 12 hours ago. The correct time now is 3 p.m. How many minutes will elapse before the clock indicates 3 p.m.?

HINT: *Sixty minutes is not the answer.*

Sixty-five minutes will elapse. The clock is 60 minutes slow after 12 hours but loses another 5 minutes before it indicates 3 p.m.

144

A City Stickler

Hints to the identity of eight nationally known cities in the United States are given below. Name each city.

Example: a president **Answer:** Washington (D.C.)

1. a saint
2. cigarettes
3. an animal
4. a sports turf
5. a U.S. state
6. an explorer
7. a quiz show
8. a stone

---

1. St. Paul, MN, St. Louis, MO, etc. 2. Winston-Salem or Raleigh, NC 3. Buffalo, NY 4. Bowling Green, KY 5. New York, NY 6. Columbus, OH 7. Truth or Consequences, NM 8. Little Rock, AR

145

It Figures

Draw the figure shown below without taking your pencil off the paper and without crossing or retracing any line.

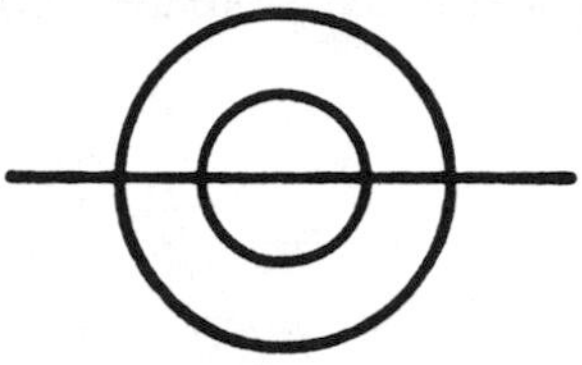

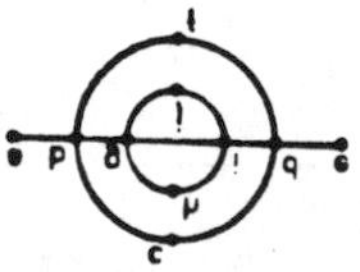

The line is drawn in the following sequence: a-b-c-d-i-h-g-i-j-g-b-f-d-e.

146

An Edgy Situation

The perforations around a postage stamp result in a pattern of alternating crests (peaks) and troughs (valleys). A certain square stamp has eleven crests and ten troughs along each edge. How many crests and troughs are there around the entire stamp?

HINT: *If you get forty-four crests, draw the stamp and count.*

There are forty crests and forty troughs. The crests at each corner must only be counted once.

147

A Notable Challenge

Insert a letter in each space to form a familiar sequence.

d_rem_fas_lat_d_

HINT: *All letters are vowels.*

The sequence is the musical scale: do re mi fa so la ti do

148

Numerical Analysis

Solve the following cross-number puzzle. All numbers are to be written as Roman numerals.

ACROSS
1. "3 down" + 13
3. An odd number
4. A number between 1 and 20.
6. No information is needed.

DOWN
1. A number between 1 and 40.
2. "5 down" multiplied by 6.
3. See "6 across."
5. "4 across" divided by 2.

HINT: *Start by analyzing "4 across" with "5 down."*

1 across is XV, 3 across is IX, 4 across is VIII, 1 down is XXVI, 2 down is XXIV, 5 down is IV. Solving procedure: (1) Using the hint, VIII is the only numeral between 1 and 20 that is four "digits" long and is evenly divisible by 2. (2) Determine the remaining numerals in this order: "2 down," "3 across," "1 across," "1 down."

149

Initially Easy

Determine the well-known initials that correspond to each hint given below.

Example: soldier **Answer:** GI

1. approaching weekend
2. reply requested
3. contagious
4. crucifixion
5. doctor
6. big shot
7. underwear
8. costly mail

---

1. TGIF 2. RSVP 3. VD 4. INRI 5. MD 6. VIP 7. BVD 8. COD

150

The End

What word or phrase is associated with the end of each of the following items?

Example: life **Answer:** death

1. a train
2. a tunnel
3. a ship (back end)
4. wine barrel contents
5. a race
6. time
7. an airplane (back end)
8. this book

---

1. caboose 2. light or opening 3. stern 4. dregs 5. finish 6. eternity
7. aft or tail 8. this puzzle

NEW

HOW SMART ARE YOU?

Have fun & find out

with Pat Battaglia's <u>new</u> book of clever word games to amaze & amuse readers of all ages.

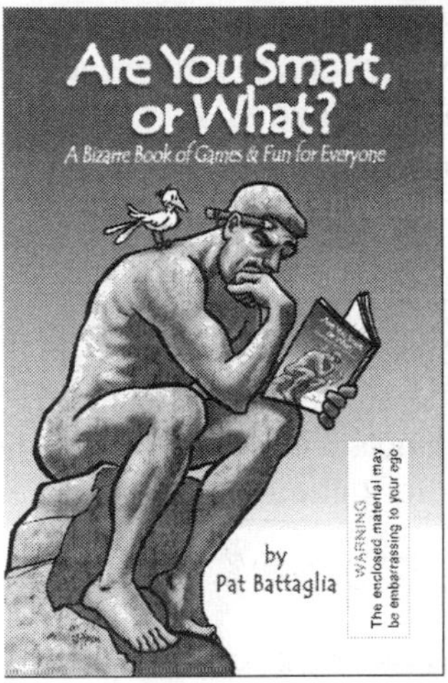

"Cleverly presented to tease, intrigue, and challenge. Naturally I scored off the charts!"

~ Bill Cosby

"I'm not all that partial to puzzles, but I had to solve almost every one in this book before I could put it aside"

~ Tom Elliott, MENSA Bulletin
MENSA: The High I.Q. Society

*"**Are You Smart, or What?** is a fascinating puzzle book of brain teasers for all ages and educational backgrounds. Challenging yet lighthearted, **Are You Smart, or What?** is the perfect gift book for puzzle enthusiasts. Highly recommended for the intellectual gamer."*

~ James A. Cox, Editor,
The Midwest Book Review

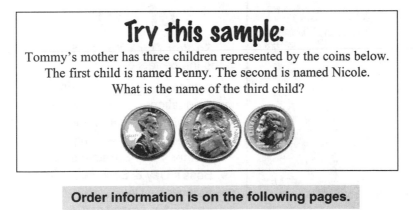

Try this sample:

Tommy's mother has three children represented by the coins below. The first child is named Penny. The second is named Nicole. What is the name of the third child?

Order information is on the following pages.

ANSWER: Tommy's mother's third child is named Tommy! What else could it be?

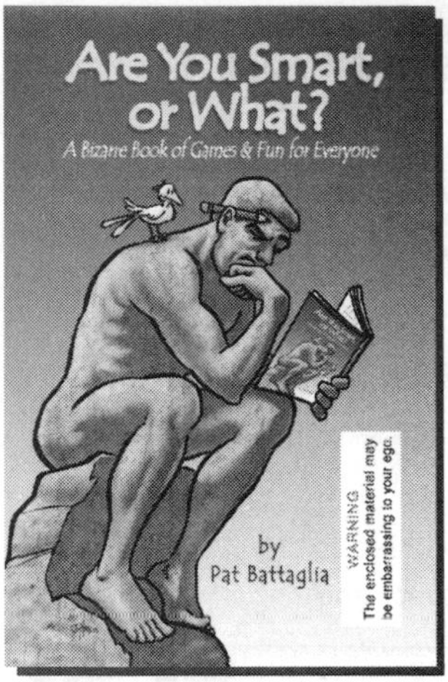

More Fun Than Ever!

Are You Smart, or What? is the most entertaining book of word games ever conceived! It combines clever challenges and surprising answers with playful innovations to amaze and amuse readers of all ages. All games are concise and uncomplicated so the entire family can enjoy them. The book includes:

- answers that are read by looking *through* the page
- amusing scoring of reader's solving ability for each game
- humorous evaluation of the reader's brain power for each section
- 3 sections: Mental Warm-ups, Mental Workouts & Mental Migraines
- special page for personalizing the book for gift giving.

To Order:

TELEPHONE: Call Toll-Free 1-866-FUN-1818 (386-1818)

ON-LINE: www.CleverPuzzles.com or www.Amazon.com

POSTAL: Use an order form on the next page. ⇨ ⇨ ⇨ ⇨

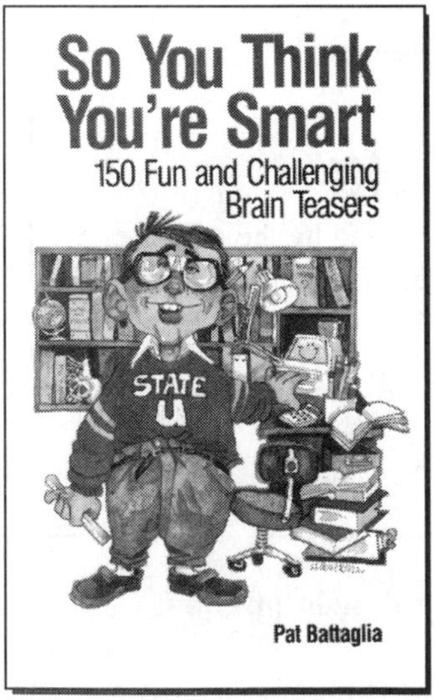

Give Gifts of Fun

So You Think You're Smart is the perfect gift for:

- birthdays
- Christmas
- graduations
- convalescents
- traveling
- parties
- vacations
- camping
- Mother's Day & Father's Day
- Boss's Day & Secretary's Day
- Valentine's Day
- just for fun on any day

Go to **www.CleverPuzzles.com** for special discounts on bulk copies for fund-raising, educational use, premiums, etc.

International Puzzle Features
4507 Panther Place, Charlotte, NC 28269

Please send copies of the following books. If I am not completely satisfied I will return them for a prompt refund, no questions asked.

______ Number of copies of **Are You Smart, or What?**
______ Number of copies of **So You Think You're Smart**
______ Total number of copies at $9.95 each .... $ ________

Shipping & Handling (total for all books ordered) ...... $ 3.00

Sales tax, NC residents only, add $0.65 per book ..... $ ________

Total amount of check or money order enclosed .... $ ________

Name ____

Address ______________________________ Apt.# _____

City ______________________ State _____ Zip _________

Make check or money order payable to International Puzzle Features

$AVE ON SHIPPING COST$

Buy multiple copies using the mail-in order form & save on shipping.

International Puzzle Features
4507 Panther Place, Charlotte, NC 28269

Please send copies of the following books. If I am not completely satisfied I will return them for a prompt refund, no questions asked.

______ Number of copies of **Are You Smart, or What?**
______ Number of copies of **So You Think You're Smart**
______ Total number of copies at $9.95 each .... $ ________

Shipping & Handling (total for all books ordered) ...... $ 3.00

Sales tax, NC residents only, add $0.65 per book ..... $ ________

Total amount of check or money order enclosed .... $ ________

Name ____

Address ______________________________ Apt.# _____

City ______________________ State _____ Zip _________

Make check or money order payable to International Puzzle Features

More Fun Than Ever!

Are You Smart, or What? is the most entertaining book of word games ever conceived! It combines clever challenges and surprising answers with playful innovations to amaze and amuse readers of all ages. All games are concise and uncomplicated so the entire family can enjoy them. The book includes:

- answers that are read by looking *through* the page
- amusing scoring of reader's solving ability for each game
- humorous evaluation of the reader's brain power for each section
- 3 sections: Mental Warm-ups, Mental Workouts & Mental Migraines
- special page for personalizing the book for gift giving.

To Order:

TELEPHONE: Call Toll-Free 1-866-FUN-1818 (386-1818)

ON-LINE: www.CleverPuzzles.com or www.Amazon.com

POSTAL: Use an order form on the next page. ⇨ ⇨ ⇨ ⇨

Give Gifts of Fun

So You Think You're Smart is the perfect gift for:

- birthdays
- graduations
- traveling
- vacations
- Christmas
- convalescents
- parties
- camping
- Mother's Day & Father's Day
- Boss's Day & Secretary's Day
- Valentine's Day
- just for fun on any day

International Puzzle Features
4507 Panther Place, Charlotte, NC 28269

Please send copies of the following books. If I am not completely satisfied I will return them for a prompt refund, no questions asked.

______ Number of copies of **Are You Smart, or What?**
______ Number of copies of **So You Think You're Smart**
______ Total number of copies at $9.95 each .... $ ________

Shipping & Handling (total for all books ordered) ...... $ 3.00

Sales tax, NC residents only, add $0.65 per book ..... $ ________

Total amount of check or money order enclosed .... $ ________

Name ____

Address ______________________________ Apt.# _____

City ____________________ State _____ Zip _________

Make check or money order payable to International Puzzle Features

So...
are you as smart as you thought you were?